Reading Comprehension with Attitude!

Incorporating higher order thinking skills
into the day-to-day reading programme
for Year 8

Book 2

Megan Roulston

essential
resources

Title:	Reading Comprehension with Attitude!
	Book 2: Incorporating higher order thinking skills into the day-to-day reading programme for Year 8
Author:	Megan Roulston
Editor:	Tanya Tremewan
Designer:	Freshfields Design Ltd
Book code:	5439
ISBN:	978-1-877536-05-2
Published:	2009
Publisher:	Essential Resources Educational Publishers Limited

United Kingdom:	Australia:	New Zealand:
Unit 8–10 Parkside	PO Box 90	PO Box 5036
Shortgate Lane	Oak Flats	Invercargill
Laughton BN8 6DG	NSW 2529	
ph: 0845 3636 147	ph: 1800 005 068	ph: 0800 087 376
fax: 0845 3636 148	fax: 1800 981 213	fax: 0800 937 825

Websites:	www.essentialresourcesuk.com
	www.essentialresources.com.au
	www.essentialresources.co.nz
Copyright:	Text: © Megan Roulston, 2009
	Edition and Illustrations:
	© Essential Resources Educational Publishers Limited, 2009

About the author: Megan Roulston has been teaching for 10 years and still loves the thrill of being at the front of the classroom each day. Believing that as teachers we all need to help and support each other no matter where we live, she started building resources from the materials and ideas she uses every day in the classroom. Megan has two wonderful boys, Cameron and Andrew. She and her husband Brett enjoy renovating houses and gardening at the weekends.

Acknowledgements: A huge thank you for all the love and support from my family: my parents, Marie and Ross Green, brother Shane and sister Kim. Last but not least, thank you to my wonderful husband, Brett. – Megan Roulston

Contents

Introduction

Our reading programmes need to empower students with a range of knowledge and skills to use in everyday life. Merely handing out a reading book from which the students answer some simple questions is a process that is likely to mean that a week later they have no idea that they have even read that book, let alone know what it was about. This *Reading Comprehension with Attitude!* series is the result of my search to move beyond that process and create reading activities that really mean something to my students.

I have used a variety of techniques to make my reading programme more interesting and therefore more beneficial to my students. Through reading every book and article given to my students over the years, I have been able to create worksheets and guided reading sessions with meaning. More meaningful activities that also incorporate higher order thinking skills have produced a reading programme with a high level of interest for my students.

Same texts, different focus – real learning!

How to use this resource

Included in this book are many A4 and A5 question templates to photocopy and then laminate. Either hand out copies of a template to individual students or groups or ask the questions orally without showing the template to the students. The templates allow both the teacher and the student(s) to focus on the desired outcome of each particular lesson.

The first templates can apply to any book students are studying:

- The "Next learning steps in reading" section contains a sheet that can be copied and stuck into the front or back of a student's reading book so that through discussion with you they can set their next learning step.

- As developing reading skills involves the use of a variety of strategies, I have adapted questions for each strategy identified in First Steps learning. If you copy and laminate these question cards and keep them next to your reading plan, you can vary the types of questions you ask students across the various books you study.

- The general questions arising from Tony Ryan's Thinker Keys and Edward de Bono's Thinking Hats, along with the templates on story setting and character profile, are also widely applicable to any book. Some of the text-specific cards that follow adapt questions based on one or more of these frameworks.

Thereafter templates offer questions related to specific books. A variety of texts are covered, including some picture books as I believe that a child is never too old for this creative genre.

The questions do not state the requirement that answers come with a full explanation and/ or specific supporting examples (quotes or scenes) from the book. It is recommended that you make this expectation clear as a matter of course when students approach any of these activities. Even on the occasions where a simple Yes or No answer is sufficient, a student needs to be able to justify it with one or more examples from the story.

For some of the books, answers are provided (as indicated by an (A) on the relevant cards). Although they offer a model of one possible approach, these answers are by no means the only possibility. Any answer that students can support fully with evidence from the text is acceptable.

Note: See the final References section for details on the editions used for the books featured in this resource.

Next learning steps in reading

I am learning to ... (Years 7 and 8)

Name: _____

○ I can select texts at my reading level to meet specific reading purposes *(to find information or to learn how to do something).*

○ I understand academic vocabulary that relates to my learning *(eg, method, identify, summarise)* and apply this to a variety of contexts.

○ I can use my knowledge of the features and structures of a wide variety of text types and forms *(eg, information, reports, embedded definitions)* to aid comprehension.

○ I can recognise a variety of grammatical constructions and some rhetorical patterns *(eg, comparison and contrast, cause and effect)* and use this knowledge to aid comprehension.

○ I can increasingly control my use of comprehension strategies in flexible ways and draw on a repertoire of such strategies when I know I am not comprehending the text fully.

○ I can use a variety of strategies to gather and synthesise information across a small range of texts *(including hypertext).*

○ I can identify and resolve issues arising from competing information.

○ I can identify and evaluate a writer's purpose *(ie, the ways that a writer uses ideas and language to suit their purpose).*

○ I can apply some criteria to evaluate texts *(eg, relevance for their purpose, accuracy of information, presence of bias).*

First Steps

Adapted from STEPS Professional Development

Reading strategies: overview

1. **Predicting**. Good readers think about what is going to happen and make predictions based on what they know and what they have read.

2. **Comparing**. Good readers make comparisons between the connections they are making, identifying the similarities and differences.

3. **Connecting**. Good readers connect what they know with what they are reading by using their background knowledge.

4. **Creating images**. Good readers imagine pictures in their heads and use their senses while they read.

5. **Determining importance**. Good readers decide what is important to read, use and learn from the texts they read.

6. **Inferring**. Good readers know how to infer when the answers are not explicitly stated in the text.

7. **Self-monitoring**. When something is confusing, good readers look closer and repair their reading.

8. **Self-questioning**. Good readers ask themselves questions when they read, as a way of learning more.

9. **Summarising and paraphrasing**. Good readers retell briefly what happened in their own words.

10. **Synthesising**. Good readers put together all of the parts to form a whole.

Predicting

(First Steps reading strategy 1)

What do you think this story will be about?

What makes you think that?

What do you think will happen?

What will happen next?

What are you guessing will happen next?

Were your predictions confirmed?

What proof/evidence do you have?

What new prediction are you making?

How have you changed/refined/adjusted your prediction?

Who will/could ...?

What will/could ...?

How will/could ...?

Which will/could ...?

Why will/could ...?

Where will/could ...?

When will/could ...?

Comparing

(First Steps reading strategy 2)

What aspects of this story are the same? What aspects are different?

How is what happens in this story the same as what you do?

How is what happens in this story different from what you do?

How is what happens in this story the same as what I do?

How is what happens in this story different from what I do?

How is this book the same as the other one I read?

How is this book the same as the other one you read?

How is this information different from what you have already read?

How is this information different from what you believe?

What information in these two books is the same?

How do these two books differ in how they present/organise/illustrate ...?

Is the information similar to or different from what you would expect? In what ways?

Connecting
(First Steps reading strategy 3)

What connections are you making?

Does this story remind you of something?

Does this story sound like something from your own life?

Is it like something you have read in another book?

Do you know someone like this character?

Have you ever felt this way?

What do you already know that will help you understand this book?

Does this information confirm or conflict with what you have read in other sources?

What do you already know about this topic?

Have you ever had an experience like this?

Can you think of something in the real world that is similar to this?

What words in this book link to words you have read in another book?

What would you expect to find in this type of book?

Creating images
(First Steps reading strategy 4)

What are the pictures/scenes in your mind as you read this book?

What do you hear/taste/smell/see/feel when you read those words?

What are you imagining at this point in the story?

What do you think the characters/settings look like in this book?

What picture in your mind are you making as you are reading right now?

What do you notice about how your senses help you to remember/understand what you have read?

What does it look like in your mind?

What is each of your senses doing as you read?

What film is playing in your head?

What words help you to visualise this text?

What words helped you form that picture?

Write/discuss what you are visualising.

Draw/sketch/create what you are visualising.

Act what you are visualising.

Determining importance

(First Steps reading strategy 5)

As you read that passage, what struck you as the most important element?

What is relevant/irrelevant to this topic?

What is essential to remember?

What evidence can you find in the book to show this element is important?

What words in the story are important for …?

How did you decide what was important?

How does the layout of the book help you to determine what is important?

When you skim the text, what important points can you find?

When you scan the page, what important facts/words/ideas do you see?

Which key words help you to understand this text?

What notes did you make as you read?

Which graphic organiser might help you to decide what is important?

Why is it important?

What/who/when/how/where could …?

Inferring

(First Steps reading strategy 6)

What/where/which/who/how/when might …?

What do you think …?

Why do you think that?

What do you think the author is telling us?

What else is the author trying to say without actually spelling it out in the story?

What words/evidence can you find in the story to support this?

What do you infer this part of the story to be about?

What is your interpretation of this text?

What strategies did you use to interpret this text?

What message do you think the author wanted to give you?

Can you weave your own idea about this story?

How did you infer the meaning of that tricky word?

What do you infer about why this character acted in this way?

Self-monitoring

(First Steps reading strategy 7)

Tell me what is happening in your head.

Does it make sense?

What word would look right?

How could you fix that?

Do you think it would help if you read on now?

Why did you slow down your reading?

How did re-reading help you?

What new questions might help you to clarify …?

What new prediction might help you to …?

What is the author saying that might help you …?

What has happened to the picture in your head?

Which character is confusing for you?

Are you discovering the answers?

Point to the last part that made sense to you.

Summarise what you have read so far.

How could you check that word?

What strategies did you use to fix up your understanding?

- -

Self-questioning

(First Steps reading strategy 8)

What is the author saying?

Why is that happening?

Why did this character …?

Is this important?

What don't you understand?

What more do you need to know?

What questions are you asking yourself?

What difficulties are you having with this text?

How does this information connect with what you have already read? How could that be?

Why do you think …?

What do you wonder …?

What else could explain …?

Where …?

When …?

Summarising and paraphrasing

(First Steps reading strategy 9)

Can you put that into your own words?

What is the main idea of this book?

What is the main idea of this paragraph?

What is discussed through this paragraph?

How would you explain what you have read to someone else?

How would you explain it simply to someone who doesn't understand?

Which key words sum up this text?

What interesting things did you find out?

Retell the story in your own words.

Which are the key events?

What was …?

Where was …?

How was …?

Why was …?

When was …?

Who was …?

Synthesising

(First Steps reading strategy 10)

How can you combine/integrate/modify …?

What could you plan/create/design/ invent …?

Retell the story from another character's point of view.

What new idea are you constructing from …?

How has your thinking changed after reading this book?

What is your plan for responding to this new information?

What strategies helped you to synthesise this information?

How can you use your own words to …?

What could …?

Where could …?

How could …?

Why could …?

When could …?

Who could …?

How would the story be different if you changed a character?

If you were the author, what would you change?

Overview of Thinkers Keys

Adapted from: Tony Ryan (1990) *Thinkers Keys for Kids*. Available for download from www.tonyryan.com.au

This section lists all the Thinkers Keys: some are more suited to reading activities than others. For examples of how this framework can be adapted to a specific book study, see activity card C of John Heffernan's *Pup* and activity card C of Harriet Graham's *A Boy and His Bear*.

Thinkers Key	What to do
The reverse	Use the words *cannot, never* and *not* in a sentence that requires you to list items.
The "What if"	Ask any "What if" question.
The disadvantages	Choose an object and list a number of disadvantages. Then state ways to correct these.
The alphabet	Compile a list of words from A to Z that are relevant to the topic.
The variations	Ask a question that starts with, "How many ways can you …?"
The prediction	Make a set of predictions about a particular situation, product or set of circumstances.
The different uses	List a wide variety of different uses for a chosen object.
The commonality	Choose two objects that generally have nothing in common and discuss some points of commonality between them.
The alternative	List ways that you could complete a task without using common tools or implements.
The combination	List two objects – one within your area of study and one outside – that are completely unrelated. Then combine the attributes into a single object.
The picture	Teacher draws a simple diagram with no relevance to the area of study and students try to work out ways to connect it to that area of study.
The ridiculous	One person makes a ridiculous statement that would be almost impossible to implement in a practical way. Others attempt to substantiate it.
The question	Start with an answer and list five questions that could only lead to that answer.
The brainstorming	State a problem (starting with "How to …") and brainstorm a list of possible solutions.
The BAR	Choose an object and propose changes to it based on the acronym: **B**igger **A**dd **R**eplace Encourage silly and innovative ideas.

Thinkers Key	What to do
The inventions	Develop inventions that are made in an unusual manner, first as an outline on paper and then as a model made out of materials.
The brick wall	Make a statement that generally would not be questioned, and then try to "break down the wall" by discussing alternatives to the situation.
The forced relationships	Develop a solution to a problem by using a number of dissimilar objects.
The interpretation	Describe an unusual situation and then think of some different reasons to explain it.
The construction	Set up a variety of construction problem-solving tasks and use lots of readily available materials.

De Bono's Six Thinking Hats

Overview

Colour	Thinking state	Direction for thinking
White	Information	What information is placed before me? What information has the text given me? No opinion or preference is stated.
Yellow	Benefits	Did any of the characters display a positive attitude? Did it benefit anyone? What were the interesting points?
Black	Judgement	I think carefully and cautiously before making any judgements about what the text has described.
Green	Creativity	What new ideas and alternatives can I generate after reading this text? I become a problem-solver and assist the characters to overcome any hurdles they may face.
Red	Feelings	What are my own feelings about the text? How can I express them to other people in a free manner?
Blue	Organisation	How could the situations that arose in the text have been avoided or changed in any way?

The questions that follow are general ones that can be applied to any fiction book. Several text-specific cards provide examples of how this framework can be applied to a specific book study (eg, activity card B of Bryce Courtenay's *Power of One*; activity card B of Michelle Magorian's *Goodnight Mister Tom*).

Reading activities using de Bono's Six Thinking Hats

 White Hat

- Complete a physical description of at least two of the main characters.
- List at least three facts you learnt from the book.
- Describe the setting(s) in the story.
- Describe the plot.

 Yellow Hat

- What were the interesting parts of the story?
- Do you think that any of the main characters displayed positive qualities? If yes, what were those qualities?

 Black Hat

- Did any of the characters make decisions that were wrong in your opinion? If yes, what were those decisions?
- Was there a problem in the story? How or why did this problem arise?

 Green Hat

- Provide a new title for the book and state why it is appropriate.
- Design a new cover for the book.
- Solve a problem that one of the characters faces.

 Red Hat

- Did any of the characters' feelings change during the story?
- How did you feel about the decisions any of the characters made in the story?

 Blue Hat

- Is there anything that the main character(s) could have done differently in the story?
- If you had been the writer of this book, which aspects of the story would you have done differently?

Story setting

When writing about the story setting, consider:

- the location of this place

- who your own readers are

- what smells a person would discover there

- what obvious sounds and more subtle sounds a person would hear

- what the person's eyes would focus on as they wandered through this place

- what objects the person could reach out and touch

- what taste a person would have left in their mouth after they have gone from this place.

Character profile

Write a profile of a character from the book that includes all of these details.

1. Make a heading with the name of the character.

2. Underneath write the book title and author's name.

3. Give a thorough physical description of this character based only on the information given in the book. You may need to make some inferences. Illustrate.

4. Describe the character's personality in five words that differ in meaning from one another. Include a quote or scene from the book that illustrates each word you have used.

5. How did the character that you have chosen hold the story together? Could the story have existed without this person?

6. If you could change one attribute about this character, what would it be and why?

7. If you could change one action of this character, what would it be and why?

8. Could you relate to the character in any way? Think about how you are similar to and/or different. Provide clear examples.

Magic Tree House series, Mary Pope Osborne

Hour of the Olympics

(Book 16)

1. Where and when did the first Olympics take place?

2. Who were the first people to write plays?

3. Why did Jack and Annie see no women or girls at the start of their adventure?

4. Which aspect of this adventure really upset Annie?

5. Do you think Annie made a smart decision by going to watch the games? Explain your answer.

6. What was the horse's name?

7. Where did Annie have to look if she ever wanted to see Pegasus again?

8. Do you think that Jack and Annie showed great bravery on this adventure? Why or why not?

9. Where do you think Morgan goes to once she has left Jack and Annie? Explain your answer.

10. How many Olympic Games have been held since the first event?

11. What are the similarities and differences between the first Olympics and the event in the 21st century?

Magic Tree House series, Mary Pope Osborne

Tigers at Twilight

(Book 19)

1. Do you think Annie is acting safely by always running off before consulting the information book?

2. Write a fact sheet about tigers. Include at least five facts and one picture.

3. Name three snakes that are poisonous.

4. Write two facts about rhinos.

5. If you could ride on the back of an animal, which animal would it be and why?

6. What does *endangered* mean?

7. Name two endangered animals. State why each one is endangered.

8. What is a *poacher*?

9. Do you think that Teddy is a smart dog? Explain your answer.

10. What is a *hermit*?

11. Why do people who are blind have good listening skills?

12. Go outside for five minutes, close your eyes and listen to the sounds around you. When you come back inside, write down all the sounds you heard.

Magic Tree House series, Mary Pope Osborne

Earthquake in the Early Morning

(Book 24)

1. What causes an earthquake?

2. What would you see, hear and smell during an earthquake?

3. What are two things you could do to look after yourself during an earthquake?

4. What could you do around your house to prepare for an earthquake so that your belongings are safer from the effects of an earthquake?

5. Why do you think there were fires after the earthquake in the story?

6. What items would you put in a survival kit?

7. Do you think moving the money was a good idea? Why or why not?

8. Do you think that Jack and Annie could have done or said anything differently so that the books would have been saved?

9. Do you think no one listened to them because they were children? Explain your answer.

10. Did Jack and Annie change history in any way? Explain your answer.

Magic Tree House series, Mary Pope Osborne

Stage Fright on a Summer Night

(Book 25)

1. What is a *magician*?

2. Where is Camelot? What is significant about it?

3. Who was King Arthur?

4. What is the name of the river in London that the bridge crossed?

5. In 1600 who was Queen of England?

6. Write down two pieces of information about the Queen of that time.

7. Did people drive cars in London at that time in history? If not, what form(s) of transport did they use?

8. Are dancing bears an acceptable form of entertainment? Explain your answer.

9. What is *stage fright*?

10. Have you ever been in a play? If so, when and why?

11. Do we use scrolls to read from today?

12. What is a *groundling*?

13. What does "All the world's a stage" mean?

14. Who was William Shakespeare?

Monday with a Mad Genius

(Book 38)

1. Who was Leonardo da Vinci?

2. Find out three facts about Leonardo da Vinci.

3. Why do you think Jack and Annie's clothes changed when they travelled?

4. What does a botanist study?

5. What is a *fresco*? What profession would you be in if you created one?

6. How many different types of noses are there (from a side-on view)?

7. Why did Jack have to hold da Vinci's notes up to the mirror?

8. Who was the mad genius?

9. Do you think he really was "mad"?

10. What did da Vinci decide the secret to happiness is?

11. Do you agree with da Vinci about the secret to happiness?

12. Write down three questions you would ask Leonardo da Vinci if you ever met him.

General questions about the series

1. Who is the cat that showed up at the tree house?

2. How do you think Jack and Annie handled the responsibility of the tree house? Answer using examples from any of the books in this series.

3. What role did Morgan have in the series?

4. What skill did Jack and Annie learn during their adventures? Use examples from any of the books in this series.

5. Do you think Jack and Annie's expeditions will ever end? Explain in detail.

6. Do you think the tree house should move so that it is possible for some other children to go on these expeditions? Answer fully.

7. How do Jack and Annie know that the tree house has arrived back?

8. Every time that Jack and Annie travel, what happens to make them fit into the place where they have travelled to?

9. When you read, do you imagine that you are in the story? Explain your answer.

10. When you are reading a book, is it important to use your imagination at the same time? Explain your answer.

11. How is reading a book just like visiting a new place?

12. What type of books do you enjoy reading? Why?

13. Complete a character profile of Jack.

14. Complete a character profile of Annie.

Beast

After Chapter 3

1. What do we learn about Jamie even on the first page of this story?

2. What is *obsessive compulsive disorder*?

3. What were Jamie's two greatest fears?

4. What or who do you think the beast is?

5. What or who is the Game Master?

6. Is Stephen a good friend?

7. Is Brendan a typical bully?

After Chapter 4

8. How did the window get broken in the bathroom?

After page 24

9. What does the story on page 24 represent or symbolise?

After reading the book: conclusion

10. What caused Brendan to be a bully?

11. How might the story have been different if Jamie had not learnt about Brendan's own problems?

12. Why do you think Jamie decided to go into the haunted house? Do you agree with his decision? Why or why not?

13. Was Jamie wise to reach out to Brendan?

14. Why was Jamie the only one who could see the weeds in the garden?

15. What is the beast?

16. Who is the Game Master and what does this role represent?

17. Does Jamie still have obsessive compulsive disorder?

18. Choose three words to describe Jamie's personality and then provide direct quotes from the story that support your choice.

19. Do you think Pudding understands Jamie's behaviour?

20. Do you think Jamie's parents completely understand him?

21. Which age group do you think this story is most suited to? Why?

Indian in the Cupboard

(Book 1)

1. Why do you think the cupboard could make only plastic items real?

2. Do you think that Omri handled his responsibility of this special gift in a positive or negative way? Provide quotes or examples from the story to support your answer.

3. Omri stated, "although grown ups usually knew what to do, what they did was very seldom what children wanted to be done". What did Omri mean? Provide an example from the story that illustrates his point.

4. Do you think the Indian illustrated how brave he was when Omri brought him to life? Use quotes or examples to support your answer.

5. Do you think that Indians (now known as Native Americans) are resourceful people? Justify your answer.

6. Complete a Plus Minus Interesting (PMI) chart about whether it is a good idea to bring plastic toys to life. Write at least three items in each column.

7. If you could choose one plastic item to bring to life, which one would it be? Why would you choose it?

8. In Chapter 8 do you think that Patrick was being respectful of Omri's wishes? Why or why not?

9. Who do you think is more responsible: Patrick or Omri? Justify your choice with direct quotes or examples from the story.

10. Would you prefer to have the live Indian or the live cowboy? Explain your answer.

11. Write three words that you think describe Little Bull's personality. Use direct quotes or examples from the story to support each word you have chosen.

12. Write three words that you think describe Boone's personality. Use direct quotes or examples from the story to support each word you have chosen.

13. What did Omri mean in Chapter 12 when he said that Patrick "was not a fit person to have charge of them"?

14. What do you think it would be like for Patrick and Omri if they could travel back to the time of Boone and Little Bull?

15. Discuss whether Omri did the right thing by giving his mother the key.

16. Do you consider anyone in this story to be a hero? Why or why not? Use direct quotes or scenes from the book to justify your answer.

17. Did you enjoy this book? Why or why not?

18. Would you like to read the other books in this series? Why or why not?

Indian in the Cupboard series, Lynne Reid Banks

The Key to the Indian

(Book 5)

1. In what way was Omri's dad acting like a child? Refer to Chapter 6.

2. The Indians (now called Native Americans) were referred to as "savages". Who were the savages really? Explain your answer.

3. Complete a character profile of:
   - Omri
   - Omri's dad
   - Little Bull.

4. In your own words, describe what happened to Omri when he travelled unexpectedly. How did he get to where he was?

5. If you could go back and meet a member of your own family, who would it be? Why would you choose this person?

6. Do you think that Patrick had a right to be annoyed? Why or why not?

7. Do you think it was fair of Omri to ask Patrick to visit? Why or why not?

8. Do you think the Indians or the English people had more respect for human life? Explain your answer in detail, using quotes or scenes from the story to support it.

9. Why would Omri never use the cupboard again?

10. Did you enjoy this book? Why or why not?

Gary Paulsen

The Crossing

1. What is a *border*? Why do many countries aim to control who crosses their own borders?

2. What is it about the United States that made it such a special dream for Manny?

3. Choose three words to describe Manny's personality. Use direct quotes from the book to justify your choices.

4. In what ways are Manny and Robert different?

5. What do Manny and Robert have in common?

6. Choose three words to describe Robert's personality. Use direct quotes from the book to justify your choices.

7. Why do you think Robert always referred to the "man in the mirror"?

8. Why do you think Robert drank so much?

9. Describe Manny's life before he met Robert. What were the worst hardships he faced?

10. Why do you think that Robert and Manny were drawn to each other?

11. On page 94 what did the sergeant mean by, "All of this is to mean something and it's for nothing. Only a game"?

12. What have you learnt about poverty from this story?

Gary Paulsen

Nightjohn

1. Write three words that describe how you felt after reading this book. Discuss why you felt this way.

2. If you could give the book a new title, what would you call it and why?

3. Do you think the book title could be changed to *The Power of One*? Explain your answer with examples from the book.

4. Write three words that describe Sarny's personality. Provide direct quotes that illustrate these traits.

5. Write three words that describe Mammy's personality. Provide direct quotes that illustrate these traits.

6. Write three words that describe Nightjohn's personality. Provide direct quotes that illustrate these traits.

7. Write three words that describe Waller's personality. Provide direct quotes that illustrate these traits.

8. Do you think that Mammy should have been whipped? Explain your answer.

9. Do you think that Nightjohn put Sarny at risk when he taught her how to read? Explain your answer.

10. Do you think that it was important for slaves to learn how to read and write? Explain your answer.

11. Was Nightjohn a hero? Explain your answer.

Gary Paulsen

Sarny: A Life Remembered

1. Do you think Waller deserved what happened to him? Explain your answer.

2. Do you think this book signifies an important time in history? Explain your answer.

3. Identify at least one way in which Sarny benefits from being able to read.

4. Do you think Sarny received what she deserved? Explain your answer.

5. Do you think Miss Laura was an intelligent woman? Explain your answer.

6. Do you think Sarny led a full life? Explain your answer.

7. If you were Sarny, would you have any regrets?

8. Do you consider Sarny to be a hero? Explain your answer.

9. Choose three words to describe Sarny's personality. Use direct quotes to justify your choice.

10. Choose three words to describe Miss Laura's personality. Use direct quotes to justify your choice.

Robert Westall

The Kingdom by the Sea

1. What is the significance of the title of this book?

2. Do you believe that Harry is a better person because of his adventure or would it have been better if he had remembered about the neighbours being away at the time of the bombing? Discuss fully.

3. At the end of the story, why was Harry determined to keep his mouth shut?

4. Do you believe that Harry will stay with his family for long or will he go back to his kingdom? Discuss fully.

5. Do you think his family were pleased to see him? Discuss fully.

6. On page 208, what does "Narrow, narrow" refer to?

7. Do you think a boy of 12 years in today's world could survive what Harry did? Discuss fully.

8. Complete a character profile of each of these characters:
   - Harry
   - Mr Murgatroyd
   - Corporal Blenkinsop.

Bryce Courtenay

Power of One
Card A

1. What does this book teach us about how we should treat people of different races?

2. What is the racial issue that is described in this book? Explain in detail.

3. Is any character "a hero" in this story? Answer this question in regard to each of the following characters:
   - Peekay
   - Professor Von Vollensteen (Doc)
   - Geel Piet.

   Provide clear examples from the story to support your decision in each case.

4. Write 10 words to describe how you would be treated if you were a white person living in South Africa when it was under the apartheid system.

5. Write 10 words to describe how you would be treated if you were a black person living in South Africa when it was under the apartheid system.

6. Complete a character profile of Peekay.

7. Complete a character profile of Professor Von Vollensteen (Doc).

8. Complete a character profile of Geel Piet.

9. Choose two of these characters and complete a Venn diagram to show their similarities and differences.

Bryce Courtenay

Power of One
Card B

White Hat

1. Complete a character profile of Peekay.
2. Complete a character profile of Professor Von Vollensteen (Doc).
3. Complete a character profile of Geel Piet.
4. What event in history caused Geel Piet to be put into a camp?
5. How long was Geel Piet in the camp?

Yellow Hat

6. What good things could you say came out of Geel Piet's life?
7. What good things could you say came out of Peekay meeting Professor Von Vollensteen?
8. Which of Peekay's positive qualities did he share with others?

Black Hat

9. Did Peekay make any decisions that were wrong in your opinion? What could he have done better?
10. Choose one of the main characters from the story. Describe the problems he faced and how he overcame them.

Green Hat

11. What is the significance of the book's title?
12. What do you think would be a good alternative title for this book? Justify your choice.
13. Design a new cover for this book.

Red Hat

14. Choose three different points in the story at which Peekay was experiencing three different emotions. Explain Peekay's feelings at each of these times.
15. How do you feel about the apartheid system?

Blue Hat

16. What could Peekay have done differently? Explain your answer and the impact that these alternative actions would have had on the outcome of the story.

Ted Hughes

The Iron Man

After Chapter One

1. Why do you think the Iron Man stepped off the cliff?

2. How was it that the Iron Man could put himself back together when he was scattered all over the place?

3. Why did the Iron Man go out to sea?

After Chapter Two

4. What did the Iron Man like to eat? Why?

5. Was it a good idea to put the Iron Man in the pit?

6. Why did the town's people think he would stay buried? Were they not very bright?

After Chapter Three

7. What similes and metaphors have been used to describe the Iron Man so far?

8. Do you think Hogarth's idea was a good one? Explain your answer.

9. Make a list of all the positive and negative aspects of the situation as you see it at this point in the story.

After Chapter Four

10. What similarities and differences do you see between the responses of the characters in this story and the way the governments or people around the world choose to respond to threats?

11. What do you think the Iron Man and the space-bat-angel-dragon might represent?

12. On page 47, we read, "All spent their spare money on preparing for wars, always making bigger and better weapons". Discuss what this quote means to you.

After Chapter Five

13. On page 51, we read, "If I can prove myself stronger than you are, then you must promise to become my slave." Discuss what this quote means to you.

14. Does the challenge on page 51 (quoted above) show the strength of the sun? What might that mean for us as humans?

After finishing the book

15. What is the theme of this story?

16. If you want to change the world, what is it that you need to have – great size or importance, for example, or something else?

17. Do you think that in real life adults would listen to a child? Explain your answer.

18. If you wrote a sequel to this story, what would you call it and what would it be about?

Ted Hughes

The Iron Woman

After Chapter One

1. So far, what differences can you see between the characters of the Iron Man and the Iron Woman?

2. Do you think that it is significant that the main human character in this book is a girl not a boy?

3. What do you think might have been wrong with the eel?

After Chapter Two

4. Why do you think the Iron Woman came to Lucy?

5. Do you think Lucy is brave? Justify your answer.

6. What did the Iron Woman mean when she said, "it burns"?

7. How was it that Lucy could hear the cry of the animals?

8. Why were all the animals crying?

9. What was the Iron Woman's purpose?

After Chapter Three

10. What did the Iron Woman give Lucy the power to do?

11. Do you think Lucy was right to get Hogarth to come?

12. Do you think the Waste Factory had anything to do with causing pollution?

13. What is wrong with pollution?

14. Why do you think the Iron Man and the Iron Woman were made differently? Do you think they were made at the same time? Explain your answer.

After Chapter Four

15. Why is the Iron Woman calling the people the "ignorant ones"? Do you agree?

16. What is meant by, "Nothing will change. Only their words change"?

17. Do you think the Iron Woman will use the power of the space-bat-angel-dragon wisely? Why or why not?

After Chapter Five

18. Why did the men turn into sea creatures?

19. Why did the Iron Woman want them to get into the water?

20. Why did the women want the factory shut down?

21. Why did the men want the factory to continue to operate?

22. Do you think that it is important that we take care of our waterways? Explain your answer.

After Chapter Six

23. What do you think the "cloud" represents?

24. Were the yellow webs real, or did they represent something else? What does this tell us about what we should be doing?

John Marsden and Matt Ottley

Home and Away

1. Complete a timeline of the main events in the story.

2. What was the single event that changed everything?

3. Complete a character profile of the person telling the story (the narrator).

4. Complete a character profile of Toby.

5. In what ways did the war change the emotions and actions of each person in the story?

6. Who do you think made the drawings?

7. How did you feel at the end of this story?

8. What do you think the moral of the story is?

9. How does this book reflect the views of many governments today?

10. Do you think that events like the ones in this story could happen or have happened in real life? Why or why not?

11. What do you think would be the best way of dealing with the problem of refugees?

12. Which age group do you think this book is best suited to? Why?

Michelle Magorian

Goodnight Mister Tom
Card A

1. Rewrite the following sentences in everyday English:

   Page 251: "Wot you on abaht? She told me he wuth staying. Said he wath wicked and wuth bein' sent to an 'ome for bad boys."

   Page 252: "Thinks she's a bleedin' saint if you'll excooth me languidge."

   Page 252: "Yeh, like furnicher bein' moved arahnd."

   Page 253: "She fancies 'erself, duth ahr Missis Beech. Sheeth got the downstairs and the upstairs room."

2. Are there any characters in this story that you consider to be a "hero"? Explain fully, providing direct quotes from the story to support your answer.

3. Complete a character profile of Mister Tom.

4. Complete a character profile of William.

5. Complete a character profile of Zach.

6. How could the tragedy that happened after William returned home have been avoided?

Michelle Magorian

Goodnight Mister Tom
Card B

 White Hat

1. Complete a character profile of Mister Tom.
2. Complete a character profile of William.
3. Complete a character profile of Zach.
4. Describe Mister Tom's place.

 Yellow Hat

5. What were the benefits of William going to live at Mister Tom's?
6. What were the benefits of William meeting Zach?

 Black Hat

7. What problems in Mister Tom's past emerged during this story?
8. What was wrong with the decision that William would return to his mother?
9. Did Mister Tom resolve the problem by going after William to London? Explain your answer.

 Green Hat

10. What is the significance of the title of this book?
11. What is a good alternative title for this book? Explain your choice.
12. Design a new cover for this book. Include an illustration.

 Red Hat

13. How do you think William was feeling as he arrived at Mister Tom's?
14. How do you think Mister Tom was feeling when William arrived?
15. How do you think William was feeling when he was locked in the cupboard?
16. How do you think William will feel now that he is back with Mister Tom?

 Blue Hat

17. What could William's mum have done differently? What impact do you think these different actions would have had on the ending of the story? Be specific.

Anne Frank

The Diary of a Young Girl

1. Who was Adolf Hitler?

2. Do you think the treatment of Jews was fair or unfair? Explain your position in detail.

3. Why did the Frank family have to go into hiding?

4. Do you think Anne is an important part of history? Explain in detail.

5. Why do you think that Anne Frank's diary has become so famous?

6. How long was the family in hiding?

7. How did Anne and Margot's relationship change during their time in hiding?

8. What were the good points about the second family joining them in the Annexe? What were the difficulties?

9. Who assisted the Franks while they were in hiding?

10. Why do you think that these people were willing to assist the Franks when they would have been killed if they were caught?

11. Who found Anne's diary?

12. Did Anne survive the war?

13. Do you think that Anne had a fulfilling life? Why or why not?

14. Do you think that Anne's father did the right thing by his family? What other decision(s) might he have made?

Josephine Poole

Anne Frank
Card A

1. What is meant by "the ring between us and the approaching danger is being pulled tighter and tighter"?

2. In what way was Anne's family considered fortunate?

3. How were the Jews being discriminated against in Germany?

4. Why did the Germans harass the Jews?

5. Were the Franks safe in Amsterdam?

6. Was Mr Frank supportive of the friends that Anne and Margot had?

7. In hindsight, should Mr Frank have taken his family to another country instead of going to Amsterdam?

8. Why do you think Anne's hands trembled as she packed her satchel?

9. What purpose did Anne's diary serve for her?

10. Record a simile from the story. (A simile is an expression comparing two things using *like* or *as … as.*)

11. How long were the Franks in the Annexe?

12. How do you think Mr Frank felt when he heard that his daughters had died?

13. Complete a character profile of Mr Frank.

14. Complete a character profile of Anne.

15. Complete a character profile of Miep.

Josephine Poole

Joan of Arc

1. Record six ways in which Joan illustrated her determination.

2. Why did Joan cut her hair short?

3. What is meant by "tomorrow blood will flow out of my body above my breast"?

4. Why did the English imprison Joan?

5. Create a Y-chart to identify what it would look like, sound like and feel like to be in one of the battles that Joan fought in.

6. Create a character profile of Joan. Include direct examples from the story.

7. At the end of the book, the author suggests that Joan's death is not really the end of her story. In what way will her story continue?

8. Do you believe that Joan was really a saint or just a very brave woman? Justify your answer.

9. Find out three facts about France during the time of Joan of Arc.

10. Why do you think Joan of Arc remains a heroine to the people of France?

Davide Cali

Piano Piano

1. Is Marcolino dedicated to learning the piano? Provide evidence for your answer from the book.

2. What are some alternative uses for the piano that Marcolino thinks of?

3. What other uses for a piano can you think of?

4. Do you think Marcolino's mum has realistic expectations?

5. Can you become a grand pianist if you are only practising because your mum wants you to? Explain your answer.

6. What was Grandpa trying to do with the photos?

7. Why do you think Marcolino's mother did not tell him the whole truth about her own childhood experience of piano practice?

8. What do you think would have happened if Grandpa had not spoken up and Marcolino's mother made Marcolino continue to practise the piano?

9. At the end of the story, in what ways had the roles reversed?

10. Do you think that Marcolino is more likely to succeed at the tuba?

11. What do you think children should learn from this story?

12. What do you think parents should learn from this story?

Jacqueline Woodson

Coming on Home Soon

1. Why does Mama refer to herself as a "coloured woman"?

2. Was Mama looking forward to going away?

3. Why was Ada Ruth not supposed to keep the kitten?

4. Why would Ada Ruth want to find a rabbit or possum but in some ways be glad not to find one?

5. Write your own description of what it would feel like to be really hungry.

6. Why were women needed to work in those times?

7. How was life for women during war time different from their life during peace time in those days?

8. Was Mama away for a year?

9. Do you think Ada Ruth trusted her mama?

10. Why do you think the words "coming home soon" are repeated throughout the book?

11. Do you think the kitten will stay with them?

12. What does this statement mean: "loving me more than rain, loving me more than snow"?

Chris Van Allsburg

Zathura: A Space Adventure

1. Before the brothers played the game, what was their relationship like?

2. Did Danny easily accept what was happening?

3. Did the game involve teamwork?

4. Did Walter develop a new respect for Danny as a result of their experience?

5. What do you think Walter was going to say to Danny as the black hole swallowed him up?

6. What is a *meteor shower*?

7. What is a *black hole*?

8. Did Danny recall what had occurred?

9. Could Walter have just been dreaming?

10. Complete a character profile of Walter.

11. Complete a character profile of Danny.

12. Do you think the brothers' relationship would have changed if they had not found the game? Why or why not?

13. Complete a Plus Minus Interesting (PMI) chart about the game Danny and Walter played.

14. Make up another imaginative game that could spill over into reality.

The Dark Is Rising series, Susan Cooper

Over Sea, Under Stone

(Book 1)

1. Complete a character profile of Jane.

2. Complete a character profile of Simon.

3. Complete a character profile of Barney.

4. Complete a character profile of Merriman.

5. What do the children find that sets their adventure in motion?

6. What aspect of history is this book referring to?

7. Write a paragraph of information about the king mentioned in this book.

8. Do you think Great Uncle Merry is who he says he is? Explain your answer.

9. Who did Barney think Great Uncle Merry might be? (Look at page 210 and the pages that follow.)

10. What do we find out about the grail in this book?

11. Do you think the children could find the second manuscript? Do you think they will?

12. If you wrote a sequel to this book, what are the key events that would happen in it?

The Dark Is Rising series, Susan Cooper

The Dark Is Rising

(Book 2)

1. Complete a character profile of Will.

2. Identify two odd things that happen to Will on the day before he turns 11.

3. What happens to Will on his birthday?

4. Describe in detail the "gift" that Will has.

5. What is telepathy?

6. Did Will travel in time? Explain your answer.

7. Who are the Old Ones?

8. What do Will and Merriman have in common?

9. Who is the Walker?

10. What does the Walker give to Will?

11. Who is the Black Rider?

12. What is the significance of the title?

13. What are the six signs made of?

14. What is the significance of the signs?

The Greenwitch

(Book 3)

1. Where had the children put the grail and what happened to it?

2. How well did Will get on with the Drews when they first met? Choose three words to describe their first meeting.

3. Describe in detail the Greenwitch ceremony.

4. Draw what you think the Greenwitch might look like.

5. Why does the Greenwitch not want to take sides with either the Light or the Dark?

6. What or who is Tethys?

7. Describe how you think Will would have been feeling as he and Merriman made the journey to see Tethys.

8. What happened to Jane that had a significant influence on her?

9. What qualities does Jane have that are especially important in this story?

10. Who is Roger Toms?

11. Who was the Greenwitch's mother?

12. Do you think it would be possible to understand this story without reading the first two books in this series? What might the reader gain from reading the other two books first?

The Grey King

(Book 4)

1. Complete a character profile of Will.

2. Complete a character profile of Bran.

3. Complete a character profile of Owen.

4. Complete a character profile of John.

5. Complete a character profile of Caradog.

6. What effect does Will's illness have on him?

7. What is an *albino*?

8. What is so special about Cafall?

9. Did Cafall really kill the sheep? How do you know?

10. Who is the Grey King?

11. What laws must the Grey King obey?

12. Who are the Sleepers?

13. What woke the Sleepers up?

14. Why do you think Will became sick in the first place?

Michael Morpurgo

Waiting for Anya

White Hat

1. Locate and record the simile used on page 4.
2. Locate and record the simile used on page 6.
3. Describe the hills during the summer months.
4. Describe the hills during the winter months.
5. Complete a character profile of Jo.
6. Complete a character profile of Grandpere.
7. Complete a character profile of Benjamin.

Yellow Hat

8. What positive qualities did Widow Horcada have even though the villagers disliked her?

Black Hat

9. In your opinion, did Jo make any decisions that were wrong?

Green Hat

10. Why is the title of the book appropriate?
11. Design a new cover for the story, changing the title if you wish. Remember to include a blurb about the story on the back cover, being careful not to give away the story's ending.

Red Hat

12. How was Jo's father feeling when he returned from the war? Explain why you think he was feeling this way. Give clear examples from the story.
13. How do you think Jo would have been feeling when Anya introduced herself?

Blue Hat

14. What do you think would have happened if Hans had gone and looked into the window of the hut? Briefly outline the events that you think would have followed.
15. What could Benjamin have done to prevent the capture of Leah and himself?

Michael Morpurgo

Who's a Big Bully Then?

1. What is your definition of a *bully*?

2. Ask one of your parents and one other adult for their definition of a *bully*. Write down the answer from each of them.

3. Compare the different definitions you have recorded. What do all of them have in common? What are the differences?

4. Complete a character profile of Darren.

5. Complete a character profile of the boy telling the story (the narrator).

6. Discuss the relationship between the book title and the illustration on the cover.

7. Is Darren physically or emotionally abusing the boy? Provide an example from the story to support your answer.

8. What is a *whippet*?

9. Make up a simile that includes the word *whippet*.

10. Is the dad proud of his son's running ability? How do you know?

11. Discuss the pros and cons of the boy winning the race.

12. Do you think the boy made the right choice by winning the race? Why or why not?

13. Why do you think Darren likes being a bully?

14. Why do you think Darren became a bully?

15. Why was Darren nervous about the challenge?

16. Did the boy have a clever plan? What could have gone wrong?

17. Shouldn't the boy be feeling victorious about what happened?

18. What do you think will happen the next time Darren is at school?

19. Why do you think Darren stayed home from school?

20. Why did the bull not hurt the boy?

21. Do you think that Darren will continue to be a bully? Why or why not?

22. Do you think this book presents a realistic solution to the problem of bullying? Why or why not?

23. What do you think the boy learnt during this story?

Michael Morpurgo

The Butterfly Lion

1. What is the significance of the title and the picture on the front cover?

2. Was Basher Beaumont a bully?

3. Who is the boy telling the story (the narrator)?

4. Is this book fiction or non-fiction? Explain your answer fully.

5. Why did the narrator run away at the beginning?

6. What do you think the old lady knew about the school? Give examples from the story.

7. Do you think Bertie's mum suffered from depression? Why or why not?

8. How did the behaviour of Bertie's mum change when the lion cub arrived?

9. In what way did the lion cub have a positive influence on Bertie's life?

10. Did Bertie's father truly understand Bertie's feelings?

11. Discuss the pros and cons of being a lion in a circus.

12. Discuss the pros and cons of being a lion living in the wild.

13. How did Bertie meet the old lady?

14. Why did Bertie and Millie keep their friendship a secret?

15. How do you think Bertie felt when he was in the trenches?

16. Did Bertie get his wish to be free when he went off to war?

17. Do you think Bertie was a hero? Why or why not?

18. How do you know that the lion remembered Bertie?

19. Why would the lion at the café be an interesting sight?

20. Write a paragraph describing how you would react if you had seen the lion at the café.

21. Would you say that Bertie was a determined person? Provide an example from the story to support your answer.

22. Why was Sunday a special day for Bertie and Millie as a couple?

23. How did the narrator meet the old lady and talk with her when she was dead?

24. If you could replace the lion at the centre of this story with another animal, what would it be? How would this change affect the story?

Michael Morpurgo

Friend or Foe

1. Why did David have to leave London?

2. What does *foe* mean?

3. Was it luck that David and Tucky ended up in the same home? Explain your answer.

4. Do you think David would have had the same adventure with the German soldiers if Tucky had not been there with him? Explain your answer.

5. Who do you think had the stronger personality: Tucky or David? Provide evidence from the story to support your answer.

6. Do you think that the boys did the right thing by helping the German soldiers? Why or why not?

7. Did the boys put themselves at risk in any way? If so, how?

8. What type of people were Ann and Mr Reynolds?

9. Why do you think that the Reynolds had never had any children of their own?

10. Do you think the Reynolds did everything they could to assist the boys in settling in? Justify your answer.

11. Do you think overall the boys had a better life with the Reynolds than they would have had if they had stayed in London?

12. Why do you think the German soldier was happy to go with the boys as their prisoner?

13. Why did the German soldier not speak in English initially?

14. Why did the soldier finally decide to speak to Mr Reynolds in English?

15. Why did Mr Reynolds understand what the boys had done?

16. Why were the boys unsure about telling Ann what they had done?

17. What do you think the future holds for the two boys? Provide a detailed answer that covers the next 12 to 24 months.

18. Complete a character profile of David.

19. Complete a character profile of Tucky.

20. Complete a character profile of Mr Reynolds.

21. Who do you think the soldier the milkman found was? Why do you think that?

Michael Morpurgo

Twist of Gold

1. Find out three facts about the potato famine in Ireland.

2. Why is Sean and Annie's father in America?

3. Write a paragraph describing how you think you would have felt if you were travelling on the ship taking Sean and Annie to America.

4. Do you think Sean and Annie were lucky children? Discuss.

5. Do you think Sean and Annie are true heroes? Discuss.

6. Do you think the torc was magical? Discuss.

7. What is the significance of the title?

8. Do you think that Sean should have taken the gold from Mr Finn? Discuss.

9. What would be one thing that Annie should have learnt on this journey?

10. Complete a character profile of each of the following characters:
    - Sean
    - Little Luke
    - Martha
    - Mr Finn
    - Annie
    - Fiddler Donnelly
    - Colonel.

Roberto Innocenti

Rose Blanche
Card A

1. Why was everyone cheering for the soldiers as they went to war?

2. At the start of the war, how were the people showing optimism?

3. Initially did the war affect Rose's life in any way?

4. What were the lorries being used to transport?

5. How is red used in the illustrations in this book?

6. In your opinion, is Rose a curious child? Provide evidence for your answer from the text.

7. Why do you think the mayor always had enough to eat?

8. How did finding the camp affect Rose?

9. Why were the children at the camp wearing yellow stars?

10. Why could the children not climb over the fence?

11. What happened to Rose?

12. What happened to the children at the camp?

13. Complete a character profile of Rose.

Roberto Innocenti

Rose Blanche

Card B: Thinking Hats

White Hat

1. What war is this story set in?
2. Complete a character profile of Rose.
3. Complete a character profile of the mayor.
4. Why were the children wearing yellow stars on their clothes?
5. Describe the camp during the war as one setting of the story.
6. Describe the town as another setting of the story.
7. Describe the camp once the war was over and spring had arrived.

Yellow Hat

8. What positive qualities did Rose display throughout the story?

Black Hat

9. In your opinion did Rose make the right decision by going back to the camp instead of leaving with her mother? List the advantages and disadvantages of what she did.

Green Hat

10. How did Rose make the lives of the children at the camp better?
11. What do you suggest as an alternative title for this book? Why do you think it would be effective as a title?

Red Hat

12. How do you think Rose was feeling when she saw the camp for the first time?
13. How do you think Rose was feeling as she brought food to the children?
14. How do you think Rose was feeling when she arrived at the camp one last time?
15. How do you think Rose's mother was feeling when she couldn't find Rose?

Blue Hat

16. Was Rose's death worth it when you think of what she achieved?

Libby Hawthorn

Way Home

1. How long do you think Shane has been homeless for? What makes you think this?

2. What is unusual about the way the text in this book is set out? Explain your answer fully.

3. Why do you think the pages have a torn effect?

4. How old you think Shane is? Give examples from the story to support your view.

5. Why does Shane have angel wings? What could these symbolise?

6. Do you think Shane has a family?

7. At Shane's home why is there a picture of a house?

8. Why does Shane call the cat various names throughout the book?

9. What is at Shane's house that makes us think he likes cats?

10. Do you think Shane is a resourceful person? Explain your answer.

11. Choose five words to summarise what home means to you.

Harriet Graham

A Boy and His Bear

Card A

1. Complete a character profile of the bear cub.

2. Complete a character profile of Dickon.

3. Complete a character profile of the bear catcher.

4. Complete a character profile of Jacob.

5. Do you think that Dickon's stepfather really cared about him? Why or why not?

6. Why did some people believe that Dickon was a witch?

7. Do you think that Dickon will miss the bear now that it has gone back to the wild? Why or why not?

8. Do you think that the bear catcher got what he deserved in the end? Justify your answer.

9. Do you think that one day Dickon will return home?

10. Do you consider Rosa to be a resourceful person? Explain your answer.

A Boy and His Bear

Card B: Thinking Hats

White Hat

1. Complete a character profile of Dickon.
2. Complete a character profile of the bear cub.
3. Complete a character profile of Jacob.
4. Complete a character profile of the bear catcher.
5. State two forms of entertainment back in those days that are rarely if ever practised today.
6. Describe the plot of the story.
7. Describe the main settings within the story.

Yellow Hat

8. What positive qualities did Dickon display?
9. What positive qualities did the bear cub display?
10. What do you consider interesting about Dickon's job as an apprentice?

Black Hat

11. In your opinion, did Dickon make the right decision about not following Ned once he had discovered the bear cub?
12. In your opinion, did Dickon make the right decision in the first place to return to Bear Garden to see the cub?

Green Hat

13. If Dickon had not met the bear cub, how do you think his life would have been different?
14. How did Rosa solve the problem of being kidnapped along with Dickon?

Red Hat

15. How did you feel when Dickon was watching the she bear being attacked by the dogs?
16. How do you think Rosa felt when she was kidnapped?
17. How do you think Dickon felt when he saw the bear cub wander into the woods and knew that he would never see the cub again?

Blue Hat

18. What would you have done differently if it was you teaching a bear cub to dance?
19. Write an alternative ending for the story, in which the bear cub wanted to stay with Dickon.

Harriet Graham

A Boy and His Bear

Card C: Thinkers Keys

The reverse

State five things that you would *never* teach a bear.

The "What if"

What if it was the she bear that Dickon was able to tame?

The disadvantages

List the disadvantages of a whip.

The alphabet

Compile a list of words from A to Z that are relevant to the topic of bears.

The prediction

Predict what might have happened if Rosa had not left clues for her father to track Dickon and her.

The question

The answer is *a bear.* What is the question?

The brainstorming

List as many ways as you can think of in which Dickon and Rosa could have got back home if Rosa's dad had not found them.

The interpretation

Your friend is wandering around on all fours like a bear with a fish in his/her mouth. What possible reasons could there be for this behaviour?

The different uses

Find 10 different uses for a leather belt.

The alternative

Clearly explain an alternative to Dickon and the bear cub travelling with Sebastien and Rosa to France.

The commonality

What do a bear catcher and a school child have in common?

Colin Thompson

Looking for Atlantis

1. Do you think the child's grandfather really had seven wives, was a prince and a pirate and ate off plates of solid gold? Why or why not?

2. What is meant by "grandfather set out on his final voyage"?

3. Could you visit Atlantis if you had a closed mind?

4. Why do you think the boy felt muddled in his head?

5. Is Atlantis a real place?

6. Is Atlantis like heaven?

7. What is a name that you would like to give to a place like Atlantis?

8. Could you find Atlantis if you searched in every part of your house?

9. Can people visit Atlantis whenever they choose?

10. Do you think that the boy will now feel at rest?

11. What special skill had the grandfather taught the boy?

12. Find two examples of visual humour in the story and describe each one.

Colin Thompson

The Violin Man

1. Why do you think Oscar didn't play the violin on Christmas Day?

2. How did Oscar release his dreams?

3. Why do you think so many people dream of being someone else?

4. Do you think Oscar had a lot of money?

5. Why did Oscar prefer to play his violin outside?

6. Imagine you are standing outside listening to Oscar play. What would you hear in the music?

7. Do you think Oscar lived in the past?

8. Was Oscar lonely?

9. Is always wanting what we don't have a healthy way of thinking?

10. Why could Oscar not see Marietta in the hall?

11. Why do you think Café Max is in many of the illustrations? What does it symbolise?

12. Can you see any way of changing Oscar's life so that he finds another way of being happy or at peace?

Colin Thompson

Tower to the Sun

1. Why are there black cats on pages 4 and 5?

2. What had happened to all the fuel?

3. What came out at night? Why?

4. At the start of the story, do you think the boy really had a sense of what it used to be like when the sun shone brightly? How much could anyone really tell from a picture?

5. What is the first idea that they think about as a way to see the sun? Why won't this possibility work?

6. What rock did the tower get built on? Why was this one chosen?

7. What was used to build the tower? Why?

8. What changes happen during the time it takes to build the tower?

9. What has happened to the people's heritage?

10. Did the richest man in the world respect others?

11. Do you agree with the grandfather: was it worth spending his fortune so that everyone could see the sun?

12. Is this book about pollution? Explain your answer fully.

John Heffernan

Pup
Card A

1. Complete a character profile of Jack.

2. Complete a character profile of Pup.

3. Complete a character profile of Mr Morton.

4. Describe Mr Morton's farm from Pup's point of view.

5. In what ways was Mr Morton a bully?

6. For what reasons was Mr Morton seeking revenge?

7. Why did Jack's dad call him a wooz?

8. How was Jack being bullied at school?

9. Did using positive reinforcement help to train Pup? Support your answer with evidence from the story.

10. In what ways are Pup and Jack similar?

11. Why did Jack feel sorry for Mr Morton?

12. Was Jack an intuitive person? Explain your answer.

John Heffernan

Pup

Card B: Thinking Hats

White Hat

1. Complete a character profile of Jack.
2. Complete a character profile of Pup.
3. Complete a character profile of Mr Morton.
4. Describe the plot of the story.
5. Describe the main settings within the story.

Yellow Hat

6. What positive qualities did Jack display?
7. What positive qualities did Pup display?
8. What do you consider interesting about herding sheep?

Black Hat

9. In your opinion, did Jack make the right decision about going to rescue Pup? Explain your answer fully.
10. In your opinion, did Jack make the right decision about entering the dog trials? Explain your answer fully.
11. What were some of the problems involved in living on a farm in this story?

Green Hat

12. Do you think that Jack's life would have been better with or without Pup in it? Provide evidence from the book to support your answer.
13. How did Jack help Mr Morton to solve some of his problems?

Red Hat

14. How do you think Mr Morton was feeling when he was lying in the field under his motorbike?
15. How do you think Jack was feeling as he was about to go out in front of everyone at the dog trials?

Blue Hat

16. If you were Jack, how would you have rescued Pup from Mr Morton?

Pup

Card C: Thinkers Keys

The reverse

State five things that you would *never* teach a dog.

The "What if"

What if Jack has not rescued Pup?

The disadvantages

List the disadvantages of poison.

The alphabet

Compile a list of words from A to Z that are relevant to the topic of dogs.

The prediction

Predict what might have happened if Jack had not even tried out for the dog trials.

The question

The answer is *a dog*. What is the question?

The brainstorming

Brainstorm as many solutions to Mr Morton's loneliness as you can think of.

The interpretation

Your friend is barking like a dog. What possible reasons could there be for this behaviour?

The different uses

Find 10 different uses for a dog collar.

The alternative

Clearly explain an alternative way to get Jack interested in reading books.

The commonality

What do a rescue and a trip to a different country have in common?

Bill Wallace

Coyote Autumn

1. What is the significance of the title of this book?

2. Create a Venn diagram to show the similarities and differences between living in an apartment and living on a farm.

3. Describe the setting of this story as though you were sitting on the front porch at about 7 am.

4. In your opinion, are greyhounds good dogs to use for hunting? Discuss the pros and cons clearly.

5. What does "them coyotes are slick as a whistle" mean?

6. Discuss the advantages and disadvantages of changing schools.

7. Discuss the advantages and disadvantages of having teachers as your parents.

8. Why do you think Brad's dad felt the need to fix things up before Mr Holdbrook came for a visit? Do you think that the jobs would have still been done if Mr Holdbrook had not been coming? Why or why not?

9. Provide an example from the story that illustrates how the coyotes can be smart.

10. Create a Plus Minus Interesting (PMI) chart about having a coyote as a pet.

11. How do you think Mr Holdbrook knew about the pup?

12. What did Mr Holdbrook mean when he said, "That coyote pup will be the best pet you ever had and the worst"?

13. Create a Venn diagram outlining the similarities and differences between the two puppies.

14. Complete a character profile of Scooter.

15. Complete a character profile of Brad.

16. Complete a character profile of Button.

17. Describe Brad's relationship with Scooter. What did each of them get out of being together?

18. If Scooter could not fend for himself in the wild, why could he not go back to live with Brad?

19. Why didn't Brad's parents just buy Brad another puppy to replace Scooter?

20. Based on this story, do you think that you will ever have a coyote for a pet?

Geoffrey Malone

Torn Ear

1. Was Russet a good mother? Provide an example from the story to support your answer.

2. How did Torn Ear get his name?

3. What do foxes like to eat?

4. How do you think Torn Ear felt about catching his first rabbit?

5. Is this story about survival? Provide clear examples from the story to support your answer.

6. Was Russet correct in not sharing some of her meals with Torn Ear? What lesson was she trying to teach him?

7. What other lessons did Russet teach Torn Ear before he was out on his own?

8. Complete a character profile of Russet.

9. Complete a character profile of Torn Ear.

10. Complete a Venn diagram comparing foxes and dogs.

11. Does Torn Ear like adventure? How do you know?

12. Does Torn Ear have good instincts? Why are instincts important to a fox's survival?

13. Complete a Venn diagram comparing foxes and humans.

14. Which animal is a major enemy of the fox?

15. What is another name for a fox den?

16. What is the main theme of this book in your opinion? Explain your answer fully.

17. What did a crow consider to be a delicacy?

18. Do foxes have a good sense of direction? How do you know?

19. When did Torn Ear feel jealous?

20. Why did humans hunt foxes (and still do in some places)?

21. Based on the information in this book, do you think that foxes lead solitary lives? Provide examples from the story to support your answer.

22. How do you think Torn Ear felt when Snape was captured?

23. Do you think Torn Ear is a hero?

Selected answers

The following answers are provided for selected task cards only. They offer a model but many other approaches and opinions are possible, provided that students justify each answer with evidence from the text in question.

Beast
Margaret Wild

1. On the first page, we learn that Jamie was very careful to behave in a particular way, even when everyone else thought it was a joke.
2. Obsessive compulsive disorder is a psychiatric disorder in which people feel compelled to behave in a particular way or repeatedly perform a particular sequence of actions to make themselves feel better or safer.
3. Jamie's two greatest fears are the beast and Brendan.

4–6. *Answers not supplied: they are personal opinion at this stage in the story.*

7. Yes, Brendan is a typical bully in that he is picking on someone who is not confident and he moves around in a group.
8. The window could have broken accidentally during the night or perhaps Jamie broke it himself but he did not remember it. Later in the story we find out that Brendan visited his house at night time: maybe he broke the window by accident.
9. The story on page 24 is about Brendan's life. He was abandoned by his mother and left to live with his father. He learnt that he needed to be extremely polite and happy so that people never knew that at home he was being beaten. Brendan believed that one day when he had children of his own, he would not abandon or hurt them. He was the one moving around in a group and chasing Jamie away. He bullied Jamie so he could have his own friends as he feared being on his own. Brendan found his own place in the haunted house. There he felt safe.

10–21. *Answers not supplied.*

Sarny: A Life Remembered
Gary Paulsen

1. *Answer not supplied.*
2. Yes, the book signifies an important period when slavery came to an end and black people became educated.
3. One benefit for Sarny is that she can read papers to find out who her children have been sold to.
4. Yes, Sarny deserved to be loved and find her children, and she deserved to be left the money, because she cared for many people and took on the responsibility that Nightjohn left behind.
5. Yes, Miss Laura was clever in that she learnt to survive on her own in a man's world. She knew who to charm and who to take on. She obtained her money and then invested it wisely. She helped others with what she had and she showed respect to the people that deserved it. She was honourable with those who mattered but cheated many others.
6. Yes, Sarny led a full life because she achieved many things and helped many people. She probably couldn't have done any more.
7. Probably she would regret that she told her husband about the school being burnt.
8. Yes, Sarny could be said to be a hero as she had a major role in black people becoming educated and she was selfless in her work to help them.

9–10. *Answers not supplied.*

The Kingdom by the Sea
Robert Westall

1. When Harry was living in his Pillbox it was located by the sea and it was at this time that Harry set himself up in his own kingdom: his Kingdom by the Sea. The title also indicates how he was in charge of his own destiny: throughout his whole adventure he was making his own destiny and he believed that every place he visited was part of his kingdom. No one within his kingdom was going to tell him what to do.
2. Yes, Harry is a better person for his adventure because he learnt many new skills that will serve him well in the future. He learnt how to appreciate things more and respect those who respect him.
3. Harry wanted to keep his mouth shut as he realised that his family would never share the knowledge he had gained and he would have to try hard to pay no attention to their ignorant comments.
4. Harry will probably not go back to his kingdom because he has grown into an adult and does not wish to be treated like a child any more.
5. Yes, Harry's family probably were pleased to see him. However, they were so caught up in what they had lost and how they had worried about him that seeing him doing really well made them angry and fuelled their selfishness.
6. "Narrow, narrow" refers to Harry's family and the way they have become narrow-minded about life.
7. Perhaps a 12-year-old boy today might not have the physical skills that Harry demonstrated. Children back then had more of a survival instinct than the children today. Children back then had to do more chores and were aware of their surroundings. A child today might not have been as naive as Harry.
8. *Answer not supplied.*

Home and Away
John Marsden and Matt Ottley

1. *Answer not supplied.*

2. The single event that changed everything was war.

3. Full profile of narrator not supplied; however, describing words may include: dreamy, hopeful, watchful, protective, caring, resourceful.

4. Full profile of Toby not supplied; however, describing words may include: relaxed, hopeful, artistic, weak, sick, confused.

5. The war changed the characters in the following ways:

   Mum was busy, frazzled, helped others **then** became a provider, resourceful, weak, and eventually died.

   Dad gardened as a hobby, offered his opinion **then** became a provider, problem-solver, and eventually died.

   The narrator ("me") had plenty of dreams and expectations, was hopeful, could find siblings annoying, **then** became grateful, watchful, protective, caring, resourceful, with lowered expectations.

   Claire was musical, liked animals, was playful **then** was at the right place at the right time, became unstable, confused.

   Toby was easygoing, relaxed, a typical five-year-old **then** became weak, sick, less lively, confused, guilty, angry.

6. Toby made the drawings: they shown the events as seen through the eyes of a five-year-old.

7. *Answer not supplied.*

8. The moral of the story is that life can change at any moment and then we must face whatever is put in front of us; never give up.

9. The book reflects how many governments are unwilling to help those in desperate need and are unsympathetic towards their circumstances.

10–12. Answers not supplied.

Goodnight Mister Tom
Michelle Magorian (Card A)

1. In everyday English, the sentences might read as follows:

   Page 251: "What are you on about? She told me that he was staying. She said that he was wicked and was being sent to a home for bad boys."

   Page 252: "She thinks she is a bloody saint if you will excuse my language."

   Page 252: "Yes, it is like furniture being moving around."

   Page 253: "Mrs Beech fancies herself. She has got the downstairs and the upstairs room."

2. Mister Tom could be said to be a hero first because he took William in and second because he went to find William when he knew that something just wasn't right. He saved William from a terrible life. William could be said to be a hero because he stayed with his sister and continued to hold her even though she was dead. Although Zach offered true friendship, he couldn't be said to be a hero.

3. Full profile of Mister Tom not supplied; however, describing words may include: set in his ways, likes routine, quiet, reserved, intelligent, sensible, caring and considerate.

4. Full profile of William not supplied; however, describing words may include: quiet, reserved, terrified, tortured and timid.

5. Full profile of Zach not supplied; however, describing words may include: determined, good friend, confident and athletic.

6. *Answer not supplied.*

Anne Frank
Josephine Poole

1. The statement means Anne Frank felt that the time when she and her family would be caught was coming closer and closer and, when they were caught, who knew what would happen to them.

2. Anne's family was considered fortunate as her father had a job and they had money.

3. The Jews were being discriminated against in a variety of ways. For example, the Jewish children had to sit in a separate part of the classroom and were bullied by others. Jewish shops were also vandalised and Jews beaten up.

4. The German people harassed the Jews because Hitler told them lies about the Jews, blaming them for Germany's problems. The Germans wanted to believe Hitler's lies because they hoped Hitler would make Germany rich once again like he said he would, and they wanted someone to blame other than themselves.

5. Initially the Franks were safe in Amsterdam but that changed when German soldiers marched through the city.

6. Yes, Mr Frank was supportive of his daughters' friends, which we can tell because he told their friends funny stories and taught them games he had invented.

7. No, Mr Frank was right to take his family to Amsterdam because he had a job there and he had no way of knowing what was going to happen. He may not have got a job in another country.

   Alternative answer. Yes, Mr Frank should have taken his family to another country further away because surely they would have had enough savings to live off until Mr Frank had got a job. At least they would have been safe, free and together.

8. Anne's hands trembled because she was unsure what was going to happen to her family and she felt scared.

9. Anne's diary was a way for Anne to express her thoughts and feelings, and a place where she could express herself freely.

10. One simile is: "It was a love as sweet, and as fragile, as the flowers on the chestnut tree outside the window."

11. The Franks were in the Annexe from 6 July 1942 to 4 August 1944 – approximately two years and one month.

12. Mr Frank may have felt deep grief, alone, hurt and confused, and that it should have been him not his girls who had been killed.

13. Full profile of Mr Frank not supplied; however, describing words may include: resourceful, caring, compassionate, naïve, innocent, responsible, trustworthy, strong-willed and determined.

14. Full profile of Anne not supplied; however, describing words may include: shy, innocent, naïve, intelligent, scared, cooperative, creative, uncertain and strong-willed.

15. Full profile of Miep not supplied; however, describing words may include: helpful, determined, resourceful, careful, trustworthy and reliable.

Joan of Arc
Josephine Poole

1. Some of the ways in which Joan of Arc demonstrated her determination are: her persistence with the captain; going to see the King; recognising the King even though he was dressed as a lord; putting the fire on her standard; leading an army to battle; continuing to fight when she was injured; and challenging William Glasdale, the leader of the English army.

2. Joan probably cut her hair short because it was more practical for her active lifestyle.

3. The quote means that Joan knew that during the battle she would be wounded above her chest.

4. The English imprisoned Joan because ordinary people saw her as a heroine and a saint, making her a threat to the English king. She was part of a bargain between two kings.

5. *Answer not supplied.*

6. Full profile of Joan not supplied; however, describing words may include: brave, fearless, adventurous, privileged, good listener, intelligent, intuitive, understanding and thoughtful.

7. The author suggests that Joan's story will continue because she is a saint and, like a star, a saint shines forever.

8–9. *Answers not supplied.*

10. Joan of Arc remains a heroine perhaps because of her great bravery and belief, and her determination to protect France.

Piano Piano
Davide Cali

1. No, Marcolino is not dedicated to learning the piano. We can tell this because initially he only spends 13 minutes practising and only goes back to it when his mother orders him to.

2. Marcolino thinks the piano could be used for: karate practice; car racing; or art.

3. *Answer not supplied.*

4. No, Marcolino's mother does not have realistic expectations. She is wanting Marcolino to achieve her dreams, but it turns out those were not dreams she ever truly had anyway.

5. No, to become a grand pianist you have to want to do it yourself. The passion has to come from within.

6. Grandpa was trying to show Marcolino that his mother had never enjoyed playing the piano.

7. Perhaps Marcolino's mother was hoping that if he succeeded at piano, she wouldn't have to remember her own failures: it would help her to rewrite her own memories.

8. *Answer not supplied.*

9. At the end the roles were reversed in that Marcolino enjoyed practising his new instrument and his mum wanted him to stop practising.

10. Yes, Marcolino is more likely to succeed at the tuba because he truly wants to learn it.

11. Perhaps children should learn that it is important to find what really interests and motivates you.

12. Perhaps parents should learn that it is no use trying to get their children to achieve their own lost dreams; instead they should support their children in doing what is important to them.

Coming on Home Soon
Jacqueline Woodson

1. Mama calls herself a coloured woman because her skin is dark (brown or black).

2. No, she did not want to go away because she loved her daughter and did not want to leave her but she had to go as she needed to earn some money for them.

3. Ada Ruth was not supposed to keep the kitten as there was not enough food for it – often Ada Ruth and her grandma did not even have much food for themselves.

4. Ada Ruth would like to find an animal from the point of view that they would then have some food, but she would be glad not to find one because then they would not have to kill an animal.

5. *Answer not supplied.*

6. Most men had gone to fight in the war so women were needed to do the jobs that the men had done before the war.

7. Some different features of life for women during war time in those days were that they worked on the railroad, earned money, hunted and often had to leave their family to get a job so that they could feed their family. Women did not usually undertake these activities during peace time.

8. No, Mama was only away during the winter months.

9. Yes, Ada Ruth trusted her mama because Mama did return after all.

10. The repeated phrase helps to reassure Ada Ruth and ourselves as readers that Mama will come back.

11. Yes, the kitten will stay because Grandma still had not got rid of it by the end of the story.

12. The statement means that Ada Ruth's mama loves her more than anything else in the world.

Zathura: A Space Adventure
Chris Van Allsburg

1. Before the brothers played the game, they had a difficult relationship: Walter was irritated by Danny and didn't tolerate him well.

2. Yes, Danny quickly accepted what was happening, as illustrated by this quote from the book: "See," said Danny, "outer space."

3. Yes, in the game the brothers had to work together to solve any problems that arose. A supporting quote from the book is: "Me and you, together. We can do it."

4. Yes, Walter did respect Danny much more after playing the game, as shown when he said to his brother, "You were terrific."

5. Perhaps Walter was going to say, "I love you."

6–7. *Answers not supplied.*

8. No, Danny did not recall their experience, as shown by this quote after the game had finished: "Look," he said, "it's some kind of game."

9. It is possible that Walter dreamt it all because he might have got knocked out when things had got rough between Danny and him outside.

10. Full profile of Walter not supplied; however, describing words may include: irritated, protective, understanding and caring.

11. Full profile of Danny not supplied; however, describing words may include: youthful, playful, friendly, scared, uncertain, naïve and innocent.

12–14. *Answers not supplied.*

Waiting for Anya
Michael Morpurgo

1. On page 4 the simile is "stood up as if she was as tall as a full-grown man".

2. On page 6 the simile is "he was as pale as a ghost and should go and lie down".

3. Full description not supplied; however, describing words for the hills in summer may include: lush, green, welcoming, clouds that swallowed the valley, and winding tracks.

4. Full description not supplied; however, describing words for the hills in winter may include: dark, dreary, muddy, covered in snow, whipping wind, and steep.

5. Full profile of Jo not supplied; however, describing words may include: shy, adventurous, appreciates nature, willing to help, supportive, strong-willed and athletic.

6. Full profile of Grandpere not supplied; however, describing words may include: grumpy, uncooperative, knowledgeable, protective, obliging and instinctive.

7. Full profile of Benjamin not supplied; however, describing words may include: fearless, hopeful, appreciates nature, willing to help, supportive and strong-willed.

8. Among Widow Horcada's positive qualities are that she loves her family, is willing to try, has a strong spirit, is supportive of those she loves, does not pry into other people's business and puts herself at risk to help others.

9. Jo might have needed one person to confide in because he was carrying around a heavy burden. So perhaps he was wrong to delay his decision to confide in Grandpere as late as he did.

10. The book title is appropriate because the events in the story would not have taken place if Benjamin had not been waiting for Anya to come and meet him. In the end Jo was waiting to meet Anya too and, finally, he did so it was a fitting ending.

11. *Answer not supplied.*

12. When he returned from the war, Jo's father may have been feeling confused, finally free, useless, irritable and/or unsure because of the changes that had happened while he was away.

13. When Anya introduced herself, Jo may have been feeling surprised, amazed, disbelieving, thankful, and/or a sense of closure or peace.

14. *Answer not supplied.*

15. One thing that Benjamin could have done to avoid capture was to get Leah quickly off the donkey first.

Twist of Gold
Michael Morpurgo

1. *Answer not supplied.*

2. Their father had gone to America to find work and set up a base before sending for his family to join him.

3. *Answer not supplied.*

4. Sean and Annie were lucky from the point of view that they finally found their father and mother still alive, although they were unlucky that they had no food to eat and had to leave Ireland, the place they had always known. They were lucky to have met the kind people they did on their journey. They kept losing the torc but then they kept getting it back so perhaps that meant they were lucky too.

5. Sean and Annie certainly had the strength and will of true heroes. They gave their best and survived against all odds when many others had died. They shared their beliefs and strength with others. They succeeded in their goal of finding their father. They also saved Little Luke's life.

6. It is possible that the torc was magical as Sean did only get better once he had held it, and whenever they lost it, they always got it back. On the other hand, maybe Sean got better simply because it wasn't his time to die and maybe the children kept getting the torc back simply because they had the help of some wonderful people.

7. The title is significant because Annie said that, when they were approaching their father's house, she would put on the "twist of gold" so their father would recognise them. The torc – the foundation of their family – was a twist of gold.

8. Sean said they came to find their father and Mr Finn had come to make a fortune, therefore they had both achieved what they had set out to do. Perhaps before taking the gold the children should have found out first how much wealth their father had. Because they had helped find the gold they had a right to some of it – maybe they did not need half but at least a few sizable pieces so they would be able to live comfortably.

9. Annie should have learnt to think before she speaks.

10. *Answer not supplied.*

Rose Blanche
Roberto Innocenti (Card A)

1. People were cheering because they wanted to believe that war was good and that the men were honouring their country by fighting for it.

2. People were showing optimism by waving to the soldiers and not worrying about having to queue for a long time.

3. No, at first the war made no obvious difference to Rose's life as she did the same things as before: playing with friends, going to school, and coming home to find a hot drink ready for her.

4. The lorries were used to transport Jews.

5. Red is used for the Nazi symbol and Rose's red ribbon, signifying Rose's relationship with the war.

6. Rose seems curious because she followed the trucks and found the camp where the children were being kept.

7. The mayor always had enough to eat because the soldiers and the men in power were aiming to keep him happy so that he in turn would do anything they required.

8. After finding the camp, Rose thought only about the children there and everything she did was in an effort to get food to them. Through her efforts she in turn became thin.

9. The children were wearing stars because this was a symbol the Nazis used as a way to identify Jews.

10. The children could not climb over the fence because it was electrified.

11. Rose was shot by a soldier.

12. The children at the camp were either taken away by the Nazis or rescued by the invading armies.

13. *Answer not supplied.*

Way Home
Libby Hawthorn

1. Shane had been homeless for at least three months because he was known on the streets by the boys and the girl; he knew his way around; and he had set up a home for himself.

2. The text appears in white on a black background instead of being black text on a white background. Perhaps the reason for this presentation is to symbolise that this story is not like everyone else's.

3. The torn effect may be to symbolise that life is not always perfect, in contrast to how we sometimes assume it is.

4. Shane is somewhere between 10 and 16 years old.

5. Shane's angel wings may symbolise Shane's caring nature: even though he has no regular home, he is still a good person on the inside. The wings may also symbolise that he is a hero as he has saved the cat from life on the streets and offered it a home.

6. No, Shane does not have a family: if he did, he would be living with them.

    Alternative answer. Yes, Shane does have a family: everyone has to belong to someone but he just doesn't live with his.

7. The picture is what he dreams of – a place to call home, where he feels safe.

8. Shane calls the cat a range of names because he does not know the cat's real name.

9. At Shane's house are a picture of a cat on the wall and a carton of milk on the floor, both of which suggest that he likes cats.

10. Yes, Shane seems resourceful because he must be to provide shelter for himself and a place to stay that is safe.

11. *Answer not supplied.*

A Boy and His Bear
Harriet Graham (Card A)

1. Full profile of the bear cub not supplied; however, describing words may include: loyal, scared, strong-willed, heroic and ferocious.

2. Full profile of Dickon not supplied; however, describing words may include: loyal, dedicated, trustworthy, honest, sensitive, strong-willed and courageous.

3. Full profile of the bear catcher not supplied; however, describing words may include: evil, manipulative, dishonest, cruel and kidnapper.

4. Full profile of Jacob not supplied; however, describing words may include: loyal, trustworthy, sensible, hardworking and mature.

5. No, Dickon's stepfather did not really care about him because he just wanted Dickon out of the house and did not respect his intelligence.

    Alternative answer. Yes, Dickon's stepfather did care about him because he wanted Dickon to learn a trade so that he could earn money for his family.

6. Some people believed Dickon was a witch because he was able to calm the bear. At that time, the general view was that bears were evil and dangerous and so it was acceptable to kill them for a sport. So people reasoned that Dickon must have special magical powers to deal with such an evil creature.

7. Yes, Dickon will miss the bear because they shared a special bond and Dickon did not have many other friends.

   Alternative answer. No, Dickon will not miss the bear because he will realise it is time to move on: he has Rosa and he knows that the bear leaving is the best possible outcome.

8. Yes, the bear catcher got what he deserved because he was an evil man who caught bears to make money and he should never have kidnapped the children and the bear cub.

   Alternative answer. No, the bear catcher did not deserve what happened because he was only doing what he could to make money for himself. In those days his job was acceptable.

9. No, Dickon will not return home because he was not close to his mum and stepfather.

   Alternative answer. Yes, Dickon will return home to see his sister and Jacob again.

10. Yes, Rosa is resourceful because she knew to leave clues for her father so he could follow them.

Looking for Atlantis
Colin Thompson

1. Probably these statements were not true as the grandfather told amazing stories every time he saw the family.

2. This statement means that the grandfather died in his bed – his final voyage.

3. No, you could not go to Atlantis with a closed mind because the grandfather said, "you had to look at things with your imagination" and "Open your heart".

4. The boy felt muddled because he was still grieving for his grandfather and had not truly let his imagination go free.

5. No, Atlantis only exists in someone's imagination.

6. Atlantis is a place where you can be at peace; some say heaven is like that too so you could say Atlantis is like heaven.

7. *Answer not supplied.*

8. No, you could not find Atlantis through a physical search as it only exists in the imagination.

   Alternative answer: Yes, you could find Atlantis through a search if at the same time you opened up your mind to the possibility that it exists.

9. Yes, people can visit Atlantis whenever they choose provided that they believe in it because it only takes believing in it to get there.

10. Yes, the boy should feel at rest because he has a truly special place to visit his grandfather.

11. The grandfather had taught the boy how to see what things can look like, going beyond what they actually look like.

12. *Answer not supplied.*

The Violin Man
Colin Thompson

1. Oscar didn't play the violin on Christmas Day because he needed to have a purpose or an audience in order to play.

2. Oscar released his dreams by playing the violin, which allowed music to flow through him and his imagination to come to the front of his mind.

3. Many of us dream of being someone else because we think they have a better life than us. We always seem to want what we don't have.

4. No, Oscar probably did not have much money because he had a "borrowed suit".

5. Oscar preferred to play outside because he was closer to the people there and the image of his daughter was with him.

6. *Answer not supplied.*

7. Yes, Oscar lived in the past; he had done the same thing for years.

8. Yes, Oscar was lonely: it seems like he talked only to Albert and he longed for his daughter.

9. Always wanting what we don't have can have unexpected consequences. For example, Oscar got what he wanted and it was not like he thought it would be.

10. Perhaps Oscar could not see Marietta because all she dreamed about was dancing for her father and it didn't have to be in a fancy hall.

11. Perhaps Café Max is there because it might have been a place Oscar played in years ago or took his daughter to. It may be a symbol of allowing the imagination to flow.

12. *Answer not supplied.*

Pup
John Heffernan (Card A)

1. Full profile of Jack not supplied; however, describing words may include: calm, reliable, caring, lack of confidence, poor reader and affectionate.

2. Full profile of Pup not supplied; however, describing words may include: frightened, skittish, nervous, anxious and intelligent.

3. Full profile of Mr Morton not supplied; however, describing words may include: cruel, evil, dishonest, neglectful, lonely, confused, frightened and unhappy.

4. *Answer not supplied.*

5. Mr Morton was a bully through his ongoing cruelty to both animals and humans, his emotional and physical abuse of others and his neglect of his dogs' needs.

6. Mr Morton was seeking revenge because his wife and daughter had left him, his wife had taken his

dog Chips, Jack took his dog Pup, and Mr Morton's plan to poison Chips and Pup did not work out and Chips bit him.

7. Jack's dad called him a wooz because Jack didn't think he and Pup would do well at the sheep dog trials.

8. Jack's classmates were bullying him by repeatedly saying that he couldn't read and that he was stupid, and then laughing at him.

9. Yes, positive reinforcement helped in training because when Jack trained him without hurting him, Pup was more respectful of Jack, listened to him and did as he was asked.

10. Pup and Jack are similar in that they both respect others, they care about what happens to their friends and they know how to support a friend.

11. Jack felt sorry for Mr Morton because he knew the man was very fearful. As it says on page 105, "Mr Morton was frightened too, frightened of something so huge and uncontrollable."

12. Yes, Jack was intuitive in that he could pick up on how other people were feeling. For example, on page 105, he realised that Mr Morton was frightened.

References

The following editions were used in creating this resource.

Banks, Lynne Reid (2000) *Key to the Indian* (new ed). London: Collins.

Banks, Lynne Reid (2003) *Indian in the Cupboard* (new ed). London: Collins.

Cali, Davide (2009) *Piano Piano*. Elwood, Vic: Wilkins Farago.

Cooper, Susan (2005) *Over Sea, Under Stone* (new ed). Harmondsworth: Puffin.

Cooper, Susan (2005) *The Dark Is Rising* (new ed). Harmondsworth: Puffin.

Cooper, Susan (2005) *The Greenwitch* (new ed). Harmondsworth: Puffin.

Cooper, Susan (2005) *The Grey King* (new ed). Harmondsworth: Puffin.

Courtenay, Bryce (1998) *Power of One* (new ed). Harmondsworth: Penguin.

Frank, Anne (2007) *The Diary of a Young Girl*. Harmondsworth: Puffin.

Graham, Harriet (1996) *A Boy and His Bear*. New York: Margaret K McElderry.

Hawthorn, Libby (1995) *Way Home*. London: Red Fox.

Heffernan, John (2000) *Pup*. Gosford, NSW: Scholastic.

Hughes, Ted (2001) *The Iron Man* (new ed). London: Faber.

Hughes, Ted (2005) *The Iron Woman* (new ed). London: Faber.

Innocenti, Roberto (2004) *Rose Blanche*. London: Red Fox.

Magorian, Michelle (1999) *Goodnight Mister Tom*. Harmondsworth: Puffin.

Malone, Geoffrey (2002) *Torn Ear* (2nd ed). London: Hodder Children's.

Marsden, John and Ottley, Matt (2008) *Home and Away*. Melbourne: Lothian.

Morpurgo, Michael (1996) *The Butterfly Lion*. Melbourne: HarperCollins.

Morpurgo, Michael (2000) *Who's a Big Bully Then?* Edinburgh: Barrington Stoke.

Morpurgo, Michael (2001) *Friend or Foe* (new ed). London: Egmont.

Morpurgo, Michael (2007) *Twist of Gold* (new ed). London: Egmont.

Morpurgo, Michael (2007) *Waiting for Anya* (new ed). London: Egmont.

Osborne, Mary Pope (1998) *Hour of the Olympics*. New York: Random House.

Osborne, Mary Pope (1999) *Tigers at Twilight*. New York: Random House.

Osborne, Mary Pope (2001) *Earthquake in the Early Morning*. New York: Random House.

Osborne, Mary Pope (2002) *Stage Fright on a Summer Night*. New York: Random House.

Osborne, Mary Pope (2009) *Monday with a Mad Genius*. New York: Random House.

Paulsen, Gary (1999) *Sarny: A Life Remembered*. Turtleback.

Paulsen, Gary (2006) *The Crossing*. Scholastic Paperbacks.

Paulsen, Gary. (1993) *Nightjohn*. New York: Delacorte Press.

Poole, Josephine (1998) *Joan of Arc*. London: Hutchinson.

Poole, Josephine (2007) *Anne Frank*. London: Red Fox.

Thompson, Colin (1997) *Looking for Atlantis* (Dragonfly reprint ed). New York: Knopf.

Thompson, Colin (1999) *Tower to the Sun*. London: Red Fox.

Thompson, Colin (2003). *The Violin Man*. Sydney: Hodder Headline.

Van Allsburg, Chris (2002) *Zathura: A Space Adventure*. Boston: Houghton Mifflin.

Wallace, Bill (2000) *Coyote Autumn*. New York: Holiday House.

Westall, Robert (2002) *The Kingdom by the Sea* (new ed). London: Egmont.

Wild, Margaret (1992) *Beast*. Norwood: Omnibus.

Woodson, Jacqueline (2004) *Coming on Home Soon*. New York: GP Putnam's Sons.